THE BOOK OF TREES

*An Introduction to Botany
Through the Study of Trees*

Sean Brooks

MEMORIA PRESS

MEMORIA PRESS

www.MemoriaPress.com

THE BOOK OF TREES
An Introduction to Botany Through the Study of Trees

Sean Brooks

ISBN 978-1-61538-214-9

First Edition © 2013 Memoria Press | 0319

Illustrated by Starr Steinbach and Jessica Osborne
Cover illustration by Edward Arthur Walton

Contents

CHAPTER 1: The Beauty of Trees 5
   Why Study Trees? 5
   Plant Systems & Organs.........................6

CHAPTER 2: The Root System 8
   Types of Roots...8
   Internal Structure of a Root 11

CHAPTER 3: The Stem 13
   External Structure of the Stem 13
   Internal Structure of the Stem 18

CHAPTER 4: The Leaves 27
   External Structure of Leaves 27
   Internal Structure of Leaves 37

CHAPTER 5: Flowers 43
   Structure 43
   Perfect Flowers 45
   Pollination and Fertilization 47

CHAPTER 6: Fruits 51
   Simple Fruits...52
   Simple Fleshy Fruits............................52
   Simple Dry Fruits 54
   Aggregate Fruits 56
   Multiple Fruits......................................57
   Seed Dispersal......................................57

CHAPTER 7: Observing Trees 59

ADVANCED WORK

CHAPTER 8: Photosynthesis...67
   Periodic Table of the Elements............69

CHAPTER 9: Respiration 75

Photo Credits 83

CHAPTER 1

The Beauty of Trees

Why Study Trees?

When we step out of our front door and our lungs are filled with the richness of the fresh air, seldom do we consider the source of that gift of breath. All around us, innumerable forms of plant life provide the means that sustain the creatures that roam the earth. All life on our planet is dependent on oxygen and food for survival. However, no animal (or human) is capable of producing either. Plants have the unique ability to create food by harnessing the power of the sun's light, and can even produce the oxygen all living creatures need to breathe.

Besides the essential role plants fulfill in our planet's system of life, plants also come in many varied forms, which makes them fascinating and exciting to study. From the soft grass that slips between your toes, to climbing vines with delicious fruit, the earth is filled with interesting plants of all shapes and sizes. Still, one member of the plant kingdom sets itself apart by its size and beauty.

Towering above people and buildings, decoratively adorning front yards, trees are everywhere you look. Trees provide fruit for consumption, homes for various animal life, and the greatest amount of oxygen produced by any plant. The durable material that comes from trees—wood —can be used for anything from baseball bats to sailboats.

Cultures around the globe have integrated native trees into the folklore of their people. The age and resilience of trees have made them a symbol of wisdom and strength. The majesty of trees has made them the object of poems and stories. Considering their value and importance, it seems a worthy exercise to study the nature and attributes of trees.

Plant Systems & Organs

In order to better understand trees, we must first understand the properties of the plant family to which they belong. Plants, like all complex living organisms, are organized into systems of **organs**. Organs are structures made of tissue that perform a particular job. When multiple organs work together to complete a particular function for an organism, they are said to be a part of a **system**. The human body has many organs, divided into 11 systems. For example, some of the organs that make up the human digestive system are the esophagus, stomach, and the small and large intestine.

Plants, on the other hand, aren't nearly as complicated. Plants are easily split up into just two systems, roots and shoots. The **root system** is made up of only one organ, the **roots** themselves. The root system anchors the plant and performs the functions of absorbing water and nutrients and storing food. The **shoot system** is responsible for holding the plant upright, manufacturing food, and reproducing the plant by means of seeds. There are three organs involved in the processes performed by the shoot system: the **stem**, the **leaf**, and the **flower**.

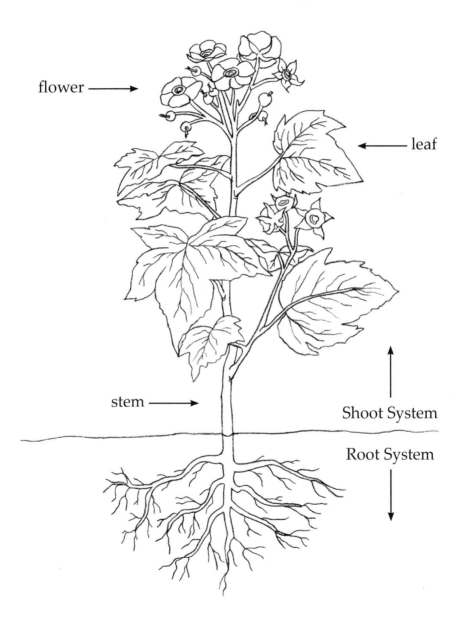

flower

leaf

stem

Shoot System

Root System

Figure 1: Root and shoot diagram

7

CHAPTER 2

The Root System

Types of Roots

Just like animals and humans, plants need food and water in order to live and grow. Although plants can produce their own food, they must get water by extracting it from the ground. The organ a plant uses to get water from the soil is its roots. Root systems for plants come in two basic designs.

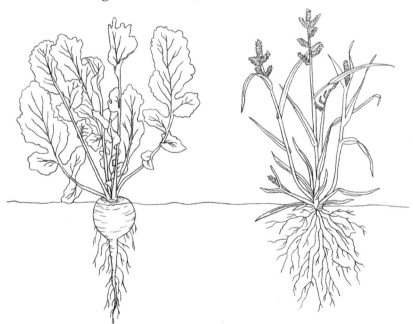

Figure 2: Taproot (left) vs. Fibrous Root (right)

The first root design is called the **taproot**. Taproots go straight down into the soil to reach higher concentrations of water. The taproot consists of one major root with relatively few roots branching from it. This primary vertical root often becomes a storehouse for food. Humans usually use the plants that have food-storage taproots as food themselves. Some examples of these types of plants are beets, carrots, and radishes.

The taproot provides structural integrity and can sometimes make a plant difficult to uproot. If you have ever tried to rid your lawn of pesky dandelions, then you know how tenacious a taproot plant can be. Oftentimes when you try to pull a dandelion, you do not get the entire taproot, which reaches far down below the surface of the ground. Unless you extract the complete taproot, the dandelion will most likely grow back.

Most plants begin their life with a taproot design. Trees, for instance, have a taproot several years into their life before the primary root is replaced with many, wide-spreading roots.

This wide-spreading mass of roots is the mark of the second type of plant root design. This root design is called a **fibrous** root system. Instead of having one primary root that plunges deep into the ground, the fibrous root system is characterized by having many thin, widespread roots that form a tangled mass just below the surface of the ground. Grasses are good examples of plants with fibrous root systems. If you try to pull up grass, you will most likely not be able to grab one individual plant. Instead, you'll have multiple plants connected together by a tangled network of thin roots. A benefit of the fibrous root system is that the tangled net of

Figure 3:
Non-Storage Taproot

9

Figure 4: Tree Root System

Figure 5: Uprooted Tree

roots helps prevent soil from being washed away, so the plant won't lose the nutrients it needs when rain comes.

The fibrous root system of a mature tree extends out in every direction in order to have as much access to water as possible. A tree's root system can be massive. In fact, a tree's root system will usually extend as wide as the tree is tall. Perhaps you've had the misfortune of running over a tree root while mowing, even when you are many feet from the trunk. These far-reaching roots are the reason why trees are so resilient and strong. If you've ever actually seen a tree knocked over, you will notice that all the earth around it gets moved as well.

Internal Structure of a Root

Regardless of the design, all roots absorb water and nutrients in the soil so that they can be transported to the rest of the plant. The moisture in the ground is brought into the root by small **root hairs** that are a part of the **epidermis** (outside layer) of the root. This water will be used by the plant to make food, and the **nutrients** (minerals and salts) that are dissolved in the water will help the tree grow.

Within the root is a bundle of tubes called the **vascular cylinder**. These tubes will conduct the water up to the stem, where it will be distributed throughout the entire plant. The term *vascular* comes from the Latin word **vasculum**, which means "little vessel." A vessel is an object that carries or transports something. Vessels in the human body, like veins and arteries, transport blood to all the organs. The vascular tissue in plants transports water and food.

The vascular cylinder is made up of two different sets of tubes. One set, called the **xylem** (zī-lem), sends the water and nutrients up to the leaves to be used in the process of making food. The **phloem** (flō-əm), the other set, transports the food made in the leaves to the rest of the plant.

The long, thin **cells** (small units of life that make up larger organisms) that make up the vascular cylinder tubes are surrounded by large, round cells that give structure and strength to the plant roots. This layer of the plant's internal structure is called the **cortex**. Besides supporting the plant root, the cortex also stores food for later use.

From outside in, then, the plant root consists of the epidermis with root hairs, the cortex, and the vascular cylinder, which contains both xylem and phloem.

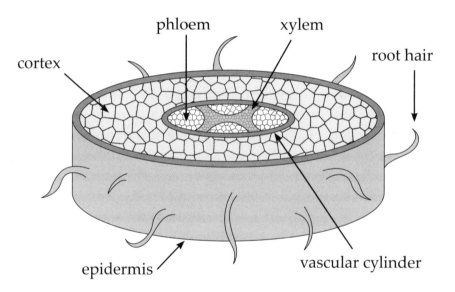

Figure 6: Inside a Root

CHAPTER 3

The Stem

External Structure of the Stem

Classification of Plants According to Stem

Once the water has been collected by the roots, it is transported to the rest of the plant through the stem. The stem is one of the three organs that make up the shoot system. The stem fulfills multiple functions for the plant. The stem supports the leaves and reproductive organs of the plant. It functions as the major highway system in the plant, distributing the food made by the leaves and the water and minerals collected by the roots. Some stems even perform the same process of making food that is done by the leaves. The stem can also act as a storage facility for food and water.

One of the ways that a plant is classified is based on the nature of its stem. Plants are put in two major categories based on whether or not their stem contains wood. All plants are made up of cells that contain cellulose. We will discuss exactly what cellulose is later, but for now, it is important to know that when the cellulose walls of a plant cell are stiffened by a compound called **lignin**, it makes the tough substance we call wood. Any plant stem that contains this substance is classified as a woody plant. Trees are easily recognized as **woody plants**. If, however, a plant does not contain wood, it is referred to as **herbaceous**. The term *herbaceous* comes from the Latin word **herba**, which means "green plant" or "grass." Often, herbaceous stems are soft and pliable, whereas woody stems are firm and stiff.

When we think about the plants we see every day, it is amazing how different each plant can look. The varying shapes and sizes of the stems are used to group land plants into four different types. Land plants (plants that live on land, as opposed to plants that live in water, like algae) are commonly classified as trees, shrubs, herbs, or vines.

Figure 7: Woody Plant   **Figure 8:** Herbaceous Plant

Trees and Shrubs

Both trees and shrubs have woody stems and are **perennial** plants. Perennial plants are plants that live more than two years. It can be said that perennial plants live "through the year," derived from the Latin word **annus**, meaning "year," and the word **per**, which means "through." Trees and shrubs also can stand erect without support. That may seem like a strange distinction, but not all plants can stand on their own. (Can you guess which type of plant stems cannot stand on their own?)

The difference between trees and shrubs is that trees have a single, tall stem, whereas shrubs have several, low stems branched near the ground. When you look at a tree, it is easy to tell which is the main stem and which are the branches. On the other hand, if you try to discern the main stem on a bush, you may only discover that you have a headache.

Figure 9: Shrub (left) vs. Tree (right)

Figure 10: From left to right: Lettuce, Wheat, Tulip, Carrot, and Grass

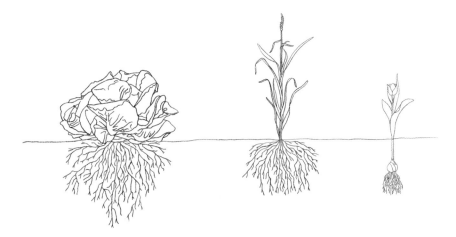

Herbs

We have already learned the term *herbaceous*, which refers to plants that don't have a woody stem. Herbaceous plants are usually referred to as simply herbs. Normally when we hear the term *herbs*, we think of something we use to add flavor to our food. Although that is one use of the term, in botany (the study of plants), it refers to all non-woody flowering plants.

Some herbs, such as potato plants or grass, are perennial like trees and shrubs. These plants flower and produce seeds each year once they reach maturity. Still, some herbs have shorter life cycles. Besides being perennial, a herb plant can be **annual** or **biennual**. An annual plant goes through its life cycle in one year (Latin **annus**, meaning "year"). This life cycle consists of germinating (the term for a seed starting to grow), flowering, producing seed, and then dying. This is why farmers who grow annuals like corn, wheat, and lettuce have to plant them each year. Sometimes an annual plant will grow in the same place the next year. This is actually not the same plant, but a new plant that has formed from one of the seeds dropped by the old plant.

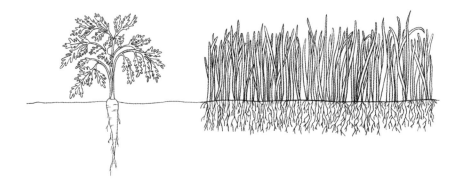

After reading the description of an annual plant, you may be able to figure out the nature of a biennial plant. A biennial plant takes two years to complete its life cycle (**bis**, the Latin word meaning "two"). Biennial plants like onions and carrots don't flower the first year, and need a spell of cold weather to initiate their flowering process. However, we don't normally see plants like carrots flower and produce seed, because we pull them from the ground while they are still in the germinating stage. This is because it is during this stage that the carrot's taproot is filled with plant food. Farmers can also "trick" some biennials that don't flower until their second year by planting them when it is still cold. This initiates the second phase of growth even though the plant hasn't been living a whole year. Extreme weather can also cause perennial plants to flower at times they normally wouldn't. One perennial plant that farmers and gardeners "trick" in order to have them grow fruit each year is the tomato plant.

Vines

If you are clever, you may have already realized the distinction that separates vines from trees and shrubs. Vines cannot stand erect without help. Vines will either spread out across the ground or use an object or another plant to support its growth. Vines that prefer to grow on the ground are called runners, while vines that prefer to scale other plants or objects are known as climbers.

An interesting (or potentially confusing) aspect of vines is that they can be either woody or herbaceous. Woody vines include grapes, kiwifruit, and ivy. Cucumbers, beans, and morning-glories are examples of herbaceous vines.

Figure 11: Climbing Vine (left) & Running Vine (right)

Internal Structure of the Stem

Herbaceous Plants

If you remember when we took a look at the internal structure of a root, we saw cells that formed tubes that transported water to the rest of the plant and brought food to the roots. We may also remember that the main difference between herbaceous and woody plants is the presence of lignin in some of the cells of the woody plants. When we move to the stem, many of the parts we learned while examining the roots will be the same. Similar parts will simply be arranged in a different way, and those arrangements will also differ between herbaceous and woody stems.

We will begin by taking a look at herbaceous plants. Starting on the outside and working our way in, we first notice a layer of thickened cells that provide protection for the inner parts of the stem. Just like the root, this outer part is called the **epidermis**. The epidermis of the stem, though, does not have root hairs. Just under the epidermis is the **cortex**, a layer of large, thinly walled cells that store food and add some structure to the stem. This, also, is similar to the plant root. Unlike the root, the plant stem contains a layer just inside the cortex called the **cambium**. The cambium is a thin ring of almost woody tissue that provides strength and stability to the stem.

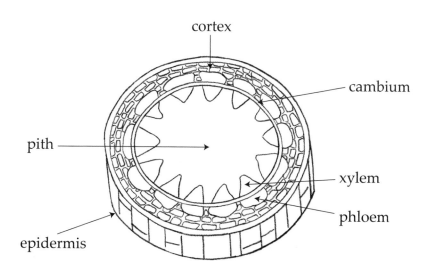

Figure 12: Internal Herb Stem

Arranged around the cambium in little bundles are the **xylem** and **phloem**. The cambium actually acts as a barrier between the two sets of tubes, with the phloem residing outside the cambium ring and the xylem within. Another unique aspect of the plant stem is a soft inner layer of tissue used for the storage of water. This spongy layer is called the **pith**.

Woody Plants - Bark

If you look at the stem of a tree (often referred to as the trunk), you will immediately observe a major difference between it and its herbaceous counterpart. Instead of a pliable epidermis, you encounter a tough layer of **bark**. Bark is a woody protective tissue that develops on mature woody plants and is a distinguishing characteristic between woody and herbaceous plants. The bark actually consists of three different layers. The outermost layer is called the **cork**. The cork is what we normally associate with tree bark. The cork looks different on various types of trees. It keeps the tree from being injured by animals or weather, and is water-proof as well. The cork of a tree is actually dead tissue and is replaced by new cork cells when it is worn or peeled off.

Below the dead layer of cork are living layers of cortex, followed by phloem. The layer of cortex cells store food for the production of more cork. The phloem cells carry the food made in the leaves downward to the growing parts of the stem and roots. The location of these tubes within the bark of a tree provides the origin of the term *phloem*. Phloem comes from the Greek word φλόος (flô-ôs), which means "bark" or "husk."

This process of transporting food throughout the tree also provides a great service to those who enjoy a tasty breakfast. The sticky substance that slowly flows through the phloem is called **sap**. The food that the leaves produce is actually a form of sugar called **glucose**. The dissolved glucose is sweet to taste. As a result, people tap trees for their sap in order to make syrup. The tree most commonly tapped for its sap is the Maple (specifically a variety of Maple called the Sugar Maple, known for its particularly sweet sap), and many a stack of pancakes has been adorned by the contents of its phloem.

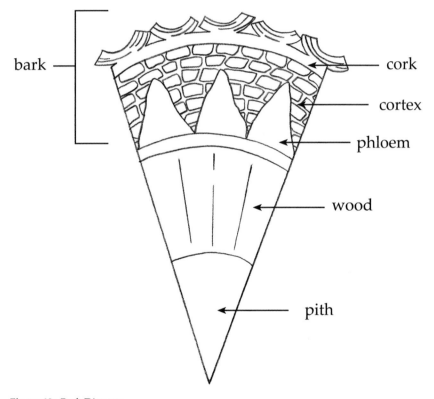

Figure 13: Bark Diagram

Bark comes in a variety of colors and textures. Most bark (like most people) starts off with a smooth outer layer. It is only when a tree has reached maturity that its bark takes on the characteristics common to its kind. Some trees maintain relatively smooth bark (like the Holly tree), while others have many fissures (cracks/splits) or furrows. The American Elm is an example of a tree that has deeply fissured bark in maturity. Other bark is scaly or flaky (Maple or Sycamore). Still other bark is rough or warty (Hackberry). The bark can also come in a number of colors. Bark can be greenish or gray and, on many trees, will become a dark brown with age. Besides the leaves and fruit, the bark is one of the most telling indicators of what type tree one is observing.

Figure 14: Types of Bark

| Fissured Bark – Elm | Flaky Bark – Sycamore | Warty Bark – Hackberry |

Smooth Bark – American Holly   Scaly Bark – Silver Maple

Wood and Pith

The stem of a woody plant is easily divided into three areas: the bark, the wood, and the pith. The first of those three areas, the bark, we have already discussed. The second, the wood, is composed of two layers. Just below the layer of cortex and phloem is a ring of growth tissue called the cambium. Just like the cambium in herbaceous stems, this cambium separates the layer of phloem and xylem. However, the cambium in a woody plant continually grows outward, making new xylem and thickening the width of the stem. Behind the cambium are the layers of xylem. Xylem is what makes up the strong, resilient inner section of the stem, which is most commonly referred to as wood. Xylem and wood are essentially the same thing. In fact, the term xylem is derived from the Greek word χυλον, which means "wood."

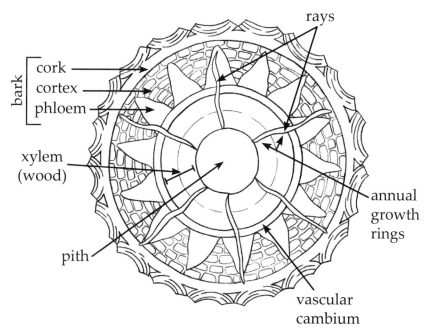

Figure 15: Woody Stem

It may seem confusing that xylem would exist in non-woody plants, but remember that the xylem cells of woody plants have the special compound lignin that makes the tough tissue we think of as wood. Although they don't form wood, the similar cells in herbaceous are called xylem because they share the same responsibility of transporting water and minerals from the roots to the leaves.

Each year the cambium adds another ring of wood growth, making the tree wider and wider each year. It does this so consistently that you can figure out the age of a tree by counting its growth rings on a cross-section of the trunk. If a tree has 20 growth rings, you know that it has been around at least 20 years. Trees can live to be hundreds and even thousands of years old. Some large sequoias in California are over 2,200 years old! The oldest living tree today is a Bristlecone Pine in California named Methuselah. A core sample of Methuselah has put his age at over 4,800 years old!

Within the layers of wood are horizontal slits called **rays**. These rays give access to the food and nutrients flowing through the phloem. After a while, some inner rings of wood stop receiving food and no longer carry water. These inner rings become hard and act almost like the backbone of the tree. These hard inner layers of wood are called **heartwood**. The outer rings of wood that still carry water are called **sapwood**. Sapwood is not quite as strong as heartwood, which is why craftsmen who cut down a tree for its wood will let the sapwood dry out before they use it.

At the very center of the woody stem is the pith. The spongy pith functions as water storage for a young stem. As the stem grows older and the growing cambium layer of wood moves farther from the center, the pith becomes less important and often disappears altogether.

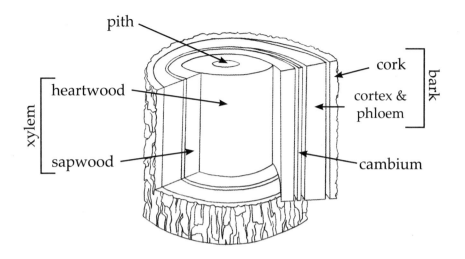

Figure 16: Parts of a Woody Stem

CHAPTER 4

The Leaves

External Structure of Leaves

Types of Leaves

As we continue to explore the shoot system of plants, we can go out on a limb and learn more about the plant organ that produces food for the plant (and, consequently, for us as well). Just like the stems of a plant, leaves come in many different shapes and sizes. Even though there are so many distinct types of leaves, scientists have divided them into two major categories: **broad-leaved** and **needle-leaved** (or scale-leaved).

A broadleaf is usually what is thought of when you speak of leaves. The majority of plants and trees have broad leaves. They are characteristically wide and flat. Examples of broadleaf plants are maple trees, ivy, and even grass. It is common, particularly among trees, for broadleaf plants to lose their leaves during the fall. This is a means for the plant to prepare for the harsh conditions of winter. It may seem strange for a plant to give up its source of food just because of the weather; however, the winter months usually have less sunlight and may contain days with heavy snow or frost. These elements make it hard for the delicate leaves to complete the process of making food. Instead, like some forest animals, the plant will store up food and go into a state of hibernation. The plant sheds its leaves and stores up the minerals the leaves produce when they decompose.

Plants that go through this process of shedding their leaves each fall are called **deciduous** plants. This primarily refers to trees because they are perennial. Annual plants aren't simply losing their leaves when winter comes; they are actually dying—the decaying former plant providing food and minerals for the new plant that will come in the spring. Though their processes do slow down, a deciduous tree is alive and well while losing its leaves. With a couple of exceptions, most broadleaf trees are deciduous.

Trees and plants that refuse to bend to the harshness of winter by shedding their leaves are called **evergreen** plants. Although there are a few broadleaf trees that are evergreen, the majority of evergreens are **conifers**. Conifers are trees that have the other leaf type, needles, and also have cones. Needle-leaves are thin and long and look like, well, needles. If you've ever had a real Christmas tree, you most likely used a conifer with needle-leaves. Pine trees, firs, and many bushes or shrubs are examples of conifers and have needle-leaves.

Figure 17: Broadleaf   **Figure 18:** Needle-leaf

Have you ever heard of someone ever referring to a tree as either being a hardwood or softwood tree? This distinction is based on whether the tree has broadleaves or needle-leaves and cones. Trees with broadleaves are commonly referred to as **hardwood**, while trees with needle-leaves are called **softwood**. This, however, is somewhat of a misnomer (a poorly given or confusing name). The type of leaf does not determine the hardness of the wood in a tree. In fact, some needle-leaf trees have wood that is harder than several broadleaf trees.

Broad Leaves

Broadleaf plants comprise the majority of land plants and offer a significant variety in terms of their leaves. A broadleaf is composed of two parts: the **petiole** (pedi-oul) and the **blade**. The petiole is the stalk that joins the leaf to the twig or branch. The petiole makes the vascular connection between the stem and the leaf, bringing water to the leaf and shipping out the food the leaf creates. There are some plants that produce leaves that don't have a petiole but grow directly from the stem. Leaves without a petiole are called **sessile** leaves. Grass provides an example of sessile leaves.

The blade is the wide, flat portion of the leaf that carries out the process of making food from sunlight and water. This process is called **photosynthesis**. We will take a closer look at the process of photosynthesis in a later chapter, but for now, it is important to know that this process requires sunlight and water. Though leaves may look and feel quite different from plant to plant, they all perform this important process.

If you do take the time to feel the leaves from multiple plants, each one will feel unique between your fingers. Some may be really smooth, while others are quite rough. The blade could be fuzzy or hairy. Others may even feel as though they have a layer of wax. These different textures are used to help classify the varying types of leaves.

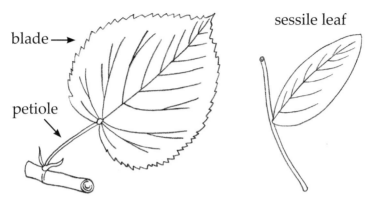

Figure 19: Leaf Parts

Leaf Shapes

Texture is just one of the many different attributes of plant leaves. To help us understand the various aspects of leaves, we can organize them in terms of their shape, arrangement, venation, margins, and whether they are simple or complex. To start, it is easily observed that leaves don't all come in the same shape. There are so many uniquely shaped leaves, it is hard to create really stringent categories for shape. To help us in our ability to observe and categorize different leaves, particularly with reference to trees, we will look at a few of the most common shapes.

A leaf can have a linear shape, meaning it is long and thin like a line. An oval-shaped leaf looks just as it sounds — like an oval. A leaf with an oblong shape is similar to an oval that has been stretched out. An ovately shaped leaf starts like an oval at the base but then rounds up to a point, resembling a pointy egg or a teardrop. A lanceolate leaf makes a narrower oval that comes to a point at the base and the tip. If you recall the long weapon with a pointed end that some Roman soldiers carried into battle, it won't be difficult to guess where the lanceolate shape gets its name. A leaf that is wider than the lanceolate, and whose point isn't as sharp, is said to be elliptical. A cordately shaped leaf looks like an upside-down heart (from the Latin **cor, cordis**), while a deltoid leaf looks like a triangle (from the Greek letter delta: Δ). Leaves that appear similar to a utensil used for flipping pancakes are said to have a spatulate shape (similar to that of a spatula).

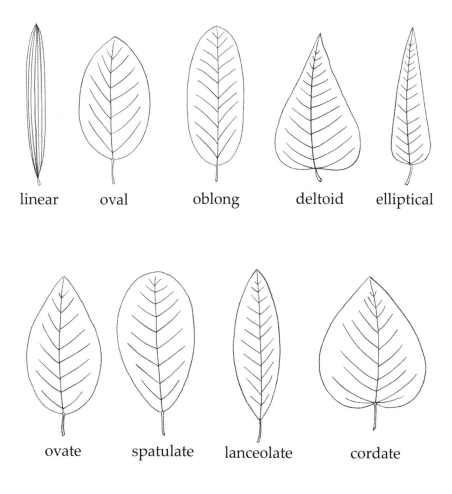

linear   oval   oblong   deltoid   elliptical

ovate   spatulate   lanceolate   cordate

Figure 20: Leaf Shapes

Arrangement of Leaves

Since sunlight is essential to the process of photosynthesis, the leaves are positioned on the stem in such a way as to maximize the amount of light to which each leaf is exposed. The arrangement of leaves on the stem comes in one of three forms: alternate, opposite, or whorled. The point at which a leaf grows from the stem is called a **node**. If only one leaf is grown at each node, the arrangement is called alternate. Usually alternate leaves do just that—alternate. A leaf will grow out to the right side of the stem, but at the next node a leaf will grow out to the left. When two leaves are grown from the same node it forms what is called an opposite arrangement. It is called opposite because the leaves grow in opposing directions even though they share the same point of origin. Some plants produce three or more leaves from each node. This arrangement is called whorled, because the leaves are positioned around the stem, somewhat resembling a fan.

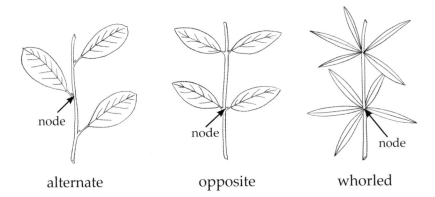

alternate   opposite   whorled

Figure 21: Leaf Arrangement

Venation of Leaves

The size and shape of the leaf is determined by how the veins are arranged in the leaf. Veins contain the vascular tissue comprised of the xylem and phloem. The veins provide structure and support for the tissue of the leaf. Veins in a human body always follow the same basic pattern, but the veins of leaves come in three varieties. The term given to the arrangement of the veins within the blade of a leaf is **venation**.

Veins sometimes run the length of the leaf without intersecting. This first type of venation is called **parallel**. Grass is a common example of parallel venation, and corn fits this description as well. The second type of venation is called **pinnate**. Pinnate venation has one major vein that runs through the center of the leaf and has smaller veins branching off it. This main vein is called the **midrib**. The term *pinnate* means "like a feather," derived from the Latin word **pinna**, meaning "feather." Some leaf blades possess multiple main veins instead of a single primary one. Multiple main veins cause the structure to be spread out and wide like the palm of your hand. This similarity gave rise to the term **palmate**, the third variation of venation.

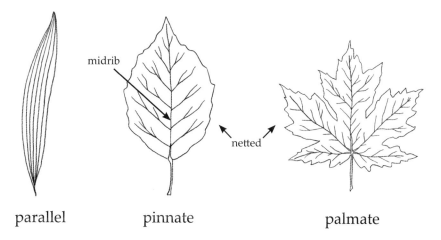

parallel   pinnate   palmate

Figure 22: Venation

Margin of Leaves

Now that we have observed the general shapes of leaves, the ways they are arranged on the stem, and the possible structures for the veins, we can discuss the **margin**. If you think back to the glorious days of coloring books, you may remember the constant encouragement to stay within the lines. That is, your teacher or parent wanted you to contain your expression of color within the limits or edge of the picture. The outer edge of a picture can be called its margin. When we speak of the margins of leaves, we are discussing the nature of the outer edge of the blade.

The margin of a blade can be entire, toothed, lobed, or some combination. The term **entire** is given to a leaf when the margin is smooth all the way around. Some leaves have smooth parts around their margins, but for a blade to be referred to as entire, it must be smooth all the way around. When a leaf blade has jagged edges, it is said to be **toothed**. A leaf can have a fine-toothed edge, a large-toothed edge, or something in between. There are even leaf margins that will have combinations of a large tooth with an attached smaller tooth. In this circumstance the margin is said to be double-toothed. There are also leaf margins with protrusions too large to be considered a tooth. These bulges are referred to as **lobes**. A leaf can have any number of lobes, and the lobes sometimes resemble fingers extending from the blade. A maple leaf is a good example of a leaf that has a large-toothed margin as well as lobes.

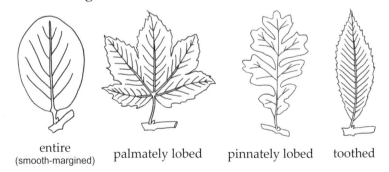

entire
(smooth-margined)   palmately lobed   pinnately lobed   toothed

Figure 23: Margin of Leaves

Figure 24: Maple Leaf (left) & Double-toothed Leaf (right)

Simple and Compound Leaves

The final aspect we can use to classify leaves is whether they are **simple** or **compound**. When it is said that a leaf is simple, it means that the leaf only has one blade on every petiole. There are some plants that seem to have smaller branches that have many leaves. However, upon closer examination, it is not a branch with many leaves but one petiole that has multiple blades. This is an example of what is called a compound leaf. In this case the multiple blades are called **leaflets**. The leaflets are not connected to a branch but a main vein called the **rachis**. Trees like the Ash and Walnut have compound leaves with long rachises and many leaflets. If it seems hard to recognize the difference between a branch with individual leaves and a compound leaf with multiple leaflets, it may be helpful to remember that a tree sheds leaves, not branches, in the fall. A compound leaf, rachis and all, will be lost when the winter approaches.

Just like venation, a compound leaf can be pinnately compound or palmately compound. If the leaflets are arranged along the sides of the stalk like a feather, they are pinnately compound. Whereas, if the leaflets all radiate from the top of the petiole, the leaf is palmately compound. There are some cases, like that of the Mimosa, in which a pinnately compound leaf actually has secondary stalks that originate from the main rachis and each have their own set of leaflets. This leaf would be considered to be bi-pinnate or twice compound. In this context, each stalk is taken to be a leaflet and each subsequent blade, a subleaflet.

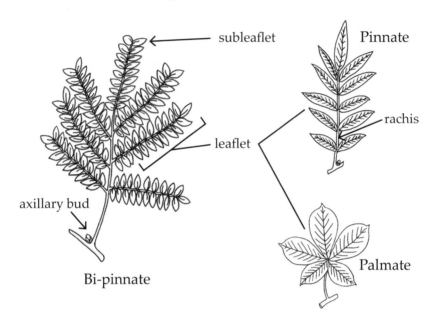

Figure 25: Compound Leaves

Leaf Buds

We've already learned that the place where the leaf connects to the branch is called the node. Every leaf grows from that node at a particular angle. The angle between the upper portion of the leaf and the branch is called the **axil**. For every leaf, particularly on a tree, there is a bud in its axil. After the leaf has fallen off, that bud will grow into either another leaf, a new branch, or a flower. The fallen leaf will leave what is called a **leaf scar** on the branch. A leaf scar has the broken ends of the vascular buddle that was supplying the leaf before it fell. Even when all the leaves have fallen, you can still see the nodes where the

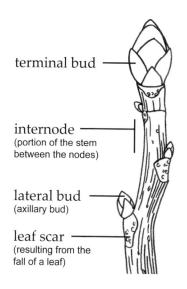

terminal bud

internode
(portion of the stem
between the nodes)

lateral bud
(axillary bud)

leaf scar
(resulting from the
fall of a leaf)

Figure 26: Leaf Buds

leaves had originated. The space in between each node is referred to as the **internode**. You will also notice buds on the sides of the branch that will grow come spring. These buds growing on the sides of the branch are called **lateral** (or axillary) **buds**. There is also, usually, a bud on the very end of the branch. This is called the **terminal bud**, because it terminates (or ends) the branch.

Internal Structure of Leaves

The main function of leaves is the production of food. The leaf is actually a food factory. No other living creature can create its own food, and thus, all life is dependent on the process that takes place within the leaf. The internal structure of the leaf has been formed perfectly to fulfill this purpose.

Though a leaf is really thin, it is actually made of multiple layers. The outermost layer is called the epidermis. The epidermis consists of a single layer of cells that provides covering and protection for the leaf. There is an epidermis layer on both the top and the bottom of the leaf. The top layer is called the **upper epidermis** and the bottom layer is called the **lower epidermis**. Both the upper and lower epidermis are coated with a waxy covering called the cuticle, which helps prevent the loss of water from the leaf.

A distinct characteristic of the lower epidermis is thousands of small leaf pores called **stomata** (singular, **stoma**). Leaves have thousands of stomata in their lower epidermis (an oak leaf can have 100,000 stomata per square inch!). These openings allow air to move into and out of the leaf. We already know that sunlight and water are necessary for the process of photosynthesis, but now we learn the third element that is required: carbon dioxide (CO_2). This chemical compound is a natural part of the air we breathe. You probably know that humans need to breathe oxygen (O_2) in order to survive. The air we take into our lungs does have plenty of oxygen to sustain us, but it also has other elements in it. One of these elements is CO_2. In fact, when humans take in air for our body's use, we take the amount of O_2 we need and expel CO_2. Humans can't use CO_2 in their bodies, and too much CO_2 can make them sick. Fortunately, the earth was designed in such a way to handle this dilemma. In the chemical process of photosynthesis, leaves take the CO_2 in the air and combine it with water drawn from the ground to make food. The result of this process is not only the creation of food but also the release of oxygen into the air.

The stomata that reside on the underside of the leaf allow CO_2 to enter the leaf and allow O_2 to escape once the food-making process is complete. The constant exchange of gases (CO_2 and O_2 are both elements that exist in a gas form) can easily dry out the leaf. That is why the stomata openings have two crescent-shaped cells called **guard cells**. These guard cells open and close the stoma in order to control the amount of gases entering and escaping the leaf, preventing the leaf from drying out. The evaporation of water from a leaf due to this exchange of gases is called transpiration. If a leaf doesn't get enough water, it won't be able to replenish the supply lost to transpiration. The result is that the leaf will wilt.

As long as a leaf has a sufficient supply of water, it will remain green in color. You may think that the green color you are used to seeing on leaves resides in these epidermal layers, but the epidermis cells are actually transparent. The color you see on a leaf comes from the mesophyll. Mesophyll cells are what comprise the middle section of the leaf blade. The term **mesophyll** comes from a combination of two Greek words: μέσος (mésos), which means "middle," and φύλλον (phyllon), which means "leaf." This middle part of the leaf has two layers of mesophyll. The upper layer of mesophyll is called the **palisade** layer. It received this name because the cells in this layer are elongated and column-like, resembling a palisade (row of columns). The lower layer of mesophyll has irregularly shaped cells separated by large air spaces. Because of this consistency, the lower mesophyll layer is called the **spongy** layer. The large spaces in the mesophyll allow air to circulate in the leaf. That way the cells come into contact with the CO_2 they need, and they can release the O_2 they produce.

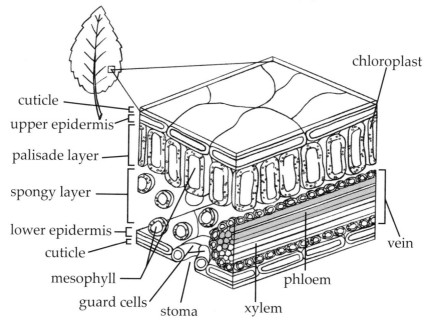

Figure 27: Internal Leaf Structure

It is within the mesophyll layers that photosynthesis takes place. Mesophyll cells contain little food factories called **chloroplasts**. These factories contain a special enzyme called **chlorophyll**, which makes the process of photosynthesis possible and gives leaves their green color. Actually, both these words originate from the Greek word for "green": χλωρός (**chloros**). Thus a chloroplast is a "green-maker" (χλωρός + πλάστης: **plastis**, meaning "one who forms") and chlorophyll is the "green-leaf-stuff" (χλωρός + φύλλον). The presence of chlorophyll is what gives leaves their green color, but plants have other colors inherent in their leaves as well. These pigments won't be seen as long as the leaf is performing the process of photosynthesis. While the leaf is manufacturing food, there is so much more chlorophyll than any other pigment that green is the only color you see. It is only when plants like trees start preparing for winter that the other colors become visible. This is because, as the weather changes, it becomes too difficult for the chloroplasts in the leaves to complete their job properly. The chlorophyll in the leaves then breaks up and disappears, leaving the other colors still present in the leaf. Each tree has its own particular pigments. This is why there are so many varieties of color during the fall.

Figure 28: Leaves that Have Changed Color

Some trees have a natural yellow pigment, while others have a vibrant red. Some even have combinations of color. Evergreens are ever-green because they are designed to continue to perform photosynthesis even in the bitter cold.

Essentially, even though the changing color of the leaves is a breathtaking and welcomed sight, it is really a process of the leaves dying. This is an intentional characteristic of deciduous trees to protect the plant during winter. In other plants, this process is usually a sign of sickness due to the inability to perform photosynthesis. A plant will wither and die if it does not have an adequate supply of water, sunlight, minerals, and CO_2.

CHAPTER 5

Flowers

Structure

Now that we have taken an in-depth look at the stem and leaves of plants, we are ready to survey the third organ of the shoot system: the flowers. Flowers may seem like a superficial form of decoration, but they actually play an essential role in the life of a plant. Flowers fulfill the role of producing seeds for the reproduction of the plant. No plant lives forever, and we have already discussed the different types of plant life cycles. In order for a type of plant to continue, it must produce more plants like itself. It is the same when it comes to humans. If humans stopped having babies, there would be no more humans. The process of producing organisms according to its kind is called **reproduction**. Flowers fulfill this process by producing seeds.

The flower itself is composed of four parts: the **sepal**, the **petals**, the **stamen**, and the **pistil**. You may recall that within the axil of a leaf a bud grows. Sometimes that bud develops into a flower. When a flower bud grows from the node, it has protective leaf-like appendages called sepals. The sepals enclose and protect the petals of the flower. When the flower blooms, the sepals open and appear like little leaves at the base of the flower.

The petals are the most noticeable part of a flower. Usually the petals are brightly colored. This colorfulness attracts insects and animals to the flower's nectar. A flower can have any number of petals. Sometimes it will have one petal that creates structure that appears trumpet-like (such as the morning-glory or petunia). A flower's collection of petals is called its **corolla**. This term comes from Latin and means "little wreath" or "little crown."

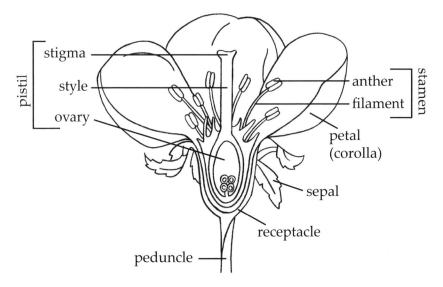

Figure 29: Flower Parts

Within the corolla are units called stamens. This is considered the male part of the flower. A flower can have few or many stamens. Stamens produce the **pollen** that is necessary for the reproduction of the plant. The stamen consist of two parts: a slender, elongated stalk called the **filament** and an enlarged structure which resides at the top of the filament called the **anther**. The anther is where pollen is produced. The filament supports the anther and supplies it with what it needs to produce the pollen. What may look like a fine powder on top of the anther is actually numerous individual grains of pollen. Each plant species has its own unique pollen structure. Pollen grains can range from smooth to knobby to spiky. Pollen is needed for the process of making seeds and is also the chief cause in the mischief of puffy eyes and runny noses, which is a result known as allergies.

In the very center of the flower is a vase-shaped structure called the **pistil**. The pistil makes up the female portion of a flower. The pistil is composed of the **ovary**, the **style**, and the **stigma**. The ovary is located at the base of the pistil. The ovary contains egg cells which will develop into seeds. Extending up from the ovary is an elongated chute called the style. The style carries the pollen collected by the stigma to the ovary. The stigma is the sticky tip of the pistil which captures the pollen. Both the male and female portions of the flower are necessary in the production of seeds.

Flowers are attached to the stem by a stalk called the **peduncle**. At the end of the peduncle is a swollen section called the **receptacle**. This base section, out of which the bloom grows, acts as a protective container for the ovary. The receptacle protects the ovary until it develops into a fruit containing the seeds. In some special cases the receptacle itself actually develops into what is considered the fruit.

Perfect Flowers

If you hear the term "a perfect flower," it probably brings to your mind an image of a gorgeous bloom that lacks any flaw. This is not exactly what botanists (those who study plants) have in mind when they refer to a perfect flower. A perfect flower, in botany (the study of plants), is a flower that has both the pollen-producing male part (stamen) and the egg-containing female part (ovary). Interestingly enough, not every flower is a perfect flower. That is not to say that there are superior and inferior flowers or that some flowers are deficient. It only means that some flowers have either stamens and no pistil, or the reverse. If a flower has the male part but lacks the female, it is said to be **staminate** (meaning "having a stamen"). On the other hand, a flower possessing a pistil but no stamen is said to be **pistillate** ("having a pistil"). Both staminate and pistillate flowers are considered **incomplete flowers**.

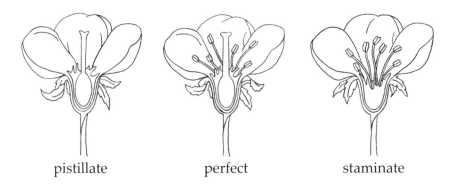

pistillate   perfect   staminate

Figure 30: Flower Types

Some plants actually contain both staminate and pistillate flowers on the same plant. Examples of trees that have both types of incomplete flowers are oaks, walnuts, and hickories. Holly trees actually have staminate and pistillate flowers on separate plants. Because of this, a holly tree is considered either male or female based on what type of incomplete flower it produces. You can tell the difference between a male and female holly tree because the female trees will have little red berries. That is, the berries will be present as long as there is a male tree nearby that can provide the necessary pollen needed for making the fruit.

Every tree that produces seeds actually has some variety of flower. This can be overlooked because not all tree flowers are as showy as, say, the magnolia or the dogwood. Many trees have inconspicuous green flowers that bloom and produce fruit unnoticed by most people. "Wait!" you might say. What about conifers? If you remember, conifers have needle-like leaves and produce special structures called **cones**. These cones are present in conifers in the place of flowers. Therefore, they are the exception to the rule because they do produce seed but don't have flowers. Similar to incomplete flowers, conifers possess cones that are either male or female. So, also, conifers can have both types of cones on the same tree, or possess one or the other. Male cones, like flowers with stamen, release pollen that is collected by the female cones in order to produce seeds. The hard, woody cones that you normally think of are actlly the female, seed-bearing cones. The male cones are much smaller and harder to notice. The male cone will actually shrivel up and die once it has released its pollen.

female

male

Figure 31: Female & Male Pinecones

Pollination and Fertilization

Both the male and female flower parts are necessary for the process of reproduction. This is because, for the egg cells in the ovary to develop into seeds, they must come into contact with the sperm cells in the pollen. **Sperm** is the technical term for the male reproductive cells. For the sperm cells to reach the eggs, the pollen must first be captured by the sticky stigma. The process in which pollen is transferred from the anther to the stigma is called **pollination**. This can happen in a variety of ways. The most common means of pollination is insects and small animals. Insects, like bees, butterflies, and moths, are attracted to the brightly colored flowers and the **nectar** they contain.

Figure 32: Bee Covered in Pollen

Nectar is a sweet-tasting, watery liquid produced by some flowers to attract insects and other animals to itself. Animals like bees and hummingbirds live on this nectar (as did the Greek gods). Bees use this nectar to make honey. The nectar is located at the base of the flower's petals. Why is this important? When a bee or hummingbird comes to a flower to enjoy a tasty meal, it has to rub up against the flower to get to the nectar. When they do this, pollen collects on their bodies. When the bee or hummingbird moves on to the next nectar stop, the pollen collected on their bodies will come into contact with the stigma as they try to reach the nectar. This type of pollination is called **biotic pollination**. We can again turn to Greek to aid us in deciphering this scientific lingo. We have already learned that *biotic* comes from the Greek word βίος, which means "life." It's the same word from which we get the term biology, which is the study of life. Biotic pollination, then, is pollination that uses a living thing to bring the pollen in contact with the stigma.

The other type of pollination occurs without the aid of a living thing. This is called **abiotic pollination**. The prefix **a** means "without" in Greek. *Abiotic* simply means "without life." So how can pollination occur without the aid of living things like insects and hummingbirds? The answer is that wind, and occasionally water, can act as an instrument in transporting pollen. Abiotic pollination is much less common than biotic pollination. Specifically, 80% of pollination is biotic, whereas only 20% is abiotic. Within that 20% of abiotic pollination, 98% is performed by wind and only 2% by water.

Once pollination has occured, the sperm cells in the pollen must make their way to the egg cells in the ovary. To accomplish this, the pollen actually grows a long tube that travels down the style. The sperm cells then travel down the pollen tube and join with the egg cells. The uniting of the sperm cell and the egg cell is called **fertilization**. The fertilized eggs will develop into seeds.

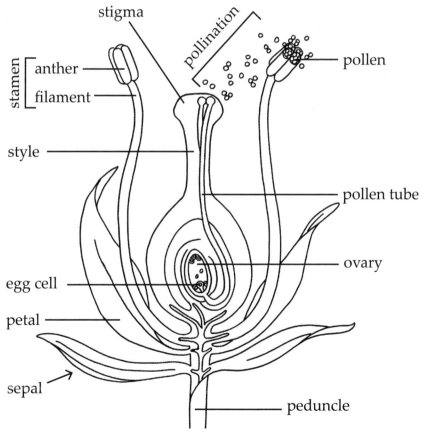

Figure 33: Fertilization

CHAPTER 6

Fruits

As the seeds develop, the ovary grows along with them. A fully developed or ripened ovary is called a **fruit**. The fruit functions as the seed-bearing structure for the plant. While the seeds are developing, the fruit offers protection. Once they are fully developed, the fruit helps distribute the seeds so they can grow into new plants. Any seed-bearing structure that develops from the flower of a plant is considered a fruit.

This definition may cause difficulties because some of the structures that fit that description aren't what you would normally consider a fruit. This is where we must make a distinction between the botanical definition (or scientific plant definition) and the **culinary** definition of fruit. The culinary definition refers to the way fruits are used in cooking. You may recognize that *culinary* derives from the Latin word **culina**, which means "kitchen." "Kitchen fruit" is a seed structure that is sweet to taste and is usually fleshy in composition. In culinary terms, seed-bearing structures that are less sweet or even savory are considered vegetables[1], and hard-shelled, oily structures are called nuts. In botanical terms, all three of these seed structures are considered fruits.

Biologists divide these fruits into three categories: **simple fruits**, **aggregate fruits**, and **multiple fruits**.

---

[1] Culinary vegetables also include edible plants or plant parts. Lettuce is a vegetable of which you eat the leaves of the plant. Carrots are a vegetable of which you eat the root. For celery you eat the stem.

Simple Fruits

Just as a flower can have any number of stamens, flowers can also have any number of pistils. When botanists divide fruit into different categories, it is based on how the fruit develops and what number of pistils (or ovaries) the flower has that produces the fruit. A simple fruit is a fruit that develops from a single flower with a single pistil. A majority of the fruits you encounter are simple fruits. Simple fruits come in two types: fleshy and dry.

Simple Fleshy Fruits

Fleshy fruits are what we normally associate with the idea of fruit. They are usually juicy and sweet and come in three varieties. The first type of fleshy fruit is the berry. A berry is fleshy and juicy throughout. Berries have an outer covering that can be soft, leathery, or somewhat hard. Grapes, oranges, cucumbers, and even watermelons are examples of berries.

Figure 34: Cucumbers, Tomatoes, and Grapes

One berry that has been the object of great debate over the years is the tomato. A vibrant struggle has taken place on many an intellectual battlefield over whether the tomato should be classified as a vegetable or a fruit. State and even national legislature has been involved in the debate.[2] The real answer to this controversial question is yes. The tomato is a savory vegetable, according to culinary practices (and the law); according to botany, the tomato is a fleshy berry, and thus a fruit.

Ironically, raspberries and strawberries are not classified as berries. They are actually what is called aggregate fruits—which we will discuss later.

Figure 35: Peach Stone

Another type of fleshy simple fruit is the **drupe**. Drupes have an outer fleshy layer and an inner woody layer called the stone. The stone (or pit) contains the seeds. Because all drupes possess a stone, they are sometimes referred to as stone fruit. Among the many kinds of drupes are peaches, plums, cherries, olives, and apricots. Almonds, walnuts, and pecans are drupes that are normally considered nuts. It just so happens that the stones that form around the seeds in these drupes are edible and quite nut-like. The coffee bean is actually a seed that comes from the drupe of a coffee plant.

The third type of fleshy fruit is the **pome**. Pomes have a papery core inside the fleshy layer. Apples are the most

---

[2] In the 1883 Supreme Court case of Nix vs. Hedden, it was ruled that the tomato should be classified as a vegetable in terms of custom regulations due to the way it is used and the common perception associated with it.

well-known pome, and pears fit in this category as well. If you look at the bottom of an apple, you can sometimes see the remains of the sepals, style, and stamens from the original flower. This is because a pome has the unique characteristic of being formed from the entire **receptacle** of the flower instead of just the ovary.

Figure 36: Apple Center

Simple Dry Fruits

Not all the fruits that develop from flowers are soft and juicy. Many are, in fact, hard and sometimes oily. Simple fruits that fit into the second category are considered dry fruits. Dry fruits come in five varieties: **legumes**, **samaras**, **nuts**, **achenes**, and **grains**.

A legume (leh-goom) is a simple dry fruit that consists of a pod enclosing several seeds. The pod can be herbaceous, such as for peas or beans. The pod can also be woody, like peanuts. Peanuts are another fruit that is unfortunately named, considering it is neither a pea nor a nut.

Perhaps you grew up with a maple or ash tree close to your house and have grown accustomed to the little helicopters

Figure 37: Legumes

or whirligigs that spin down from the tree during the summer. These "helicopters" are actually winged seeds called **samaras**. The papery wings of the samara slow the fall of the seed so it can drift farther from the tree.

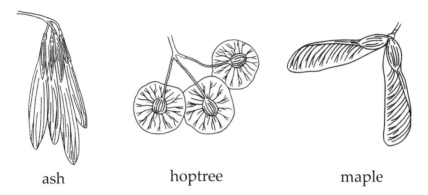

ash   hoptree   maple

Figure 38: Samaras

Figure 39: Acorns

A simple dry fruit in which the seed is enclosed by a hard covering, or shell, is called a **nut**. A true nut only has one seed for each flower. Examples of nuts include chestnuts, hazelnuts, and acorns.

Very similar to a nut, an **achene** (ə-keen) consists of a seed enclosed in a shell. Though, in the case of the achene, the shell is so thin and fits so closely that the shell is often mistaken to be the seed itself. Sunflower seeds are examples of achenes.

Figure 40: Open Sunflower Seed

One of the most important dry fruits to the human diet is the fruit of the grass family. These fruits are called **grains**. Some examples of grains are barley, oats, rye, corn, wheat, and rice. These grains are specifically referred to as cereal grains. The name given to your breakfast-bowl-of-goodness finds its origin in this grass fruit. Though grains are usually thought of as seeds, each kernel of grain is actually a complete fruit consisting of a shell and a seed. The shell of grains is quite thin, yet unlike that of nuts or achenes, it is directly attached to the seed. Because of this, grain requires a special process to separate the seed from the shell. The process is called milling. Essentially, milling takes a large stone or metal roller to break the grain open. Then the shell is removed from the grain. The fruit shell usually has little nutritional value, which is why it is removed. However, sometimes people will use the shell for fiber. The fruit-shell of wheat is called **bran**. If you eat a bran muffin, it means that some of the shell was intentionally left for fiber and taste.

Figure 41: Wheat and its Fruit

Aggregate Fruits

As we have learned, some flowers have more than one pistil. When the seeds in these flowers develop each ovary essentially produces its own fruit. Since all these fruits grow together from the same flower, the result is a fruit that is actually a cluster of individual fruit structures, each containing its own seed. These types of fruits are called **aggregate fruits**. This is the category that strawberries and raspberries rightfully inhabit.

Another example of an aggregate fruit is the blackberry, also not technically a berry. If you look at the surface of the strawberry, you will see that each tiny structure contains what appears to be a seed. These are technically achenes, which possess a seed within their thin shell.

Figure 42: Blackberries

Figure 43: Pineapple

Multiple Fruits

There are also fruits that are called **multiple fruits**. They are called multiple fruits because they are the result, not of one flower, but of many. On some plants, when groups of individual flowers develop their seeds, the ovaries actually fuse together. This produces a compound fruit. Pineapples and figs are both examples of multiple fruits.

Seed Dispersal

These various forms of fruit all help distribute the plant's seeds so that they can reproduce new plants just like themselves. Fruits like samaras use the wind to take the seeds far from the original tree. Fruits like apples and oranges fall off the tree and roll to different spots or are picked up by an animal or human that consumes the flesh and tosses the seeds aside. It is amazing to think that fruits are actually designed to need humans and animals to help them distribute their seeds. Correspondingly, humans and animals rely on fruits as an essential part of their diet.

CHAPTER 7

Observing Trees

Now that we have learned the nature of plants, we can use that information to observe and identify trees. It is important to understand the world around us. The better we know our world, the better we can operate within it. Trees play an important role in the world we inhabit and are worthy of our attention. We can employ the knowledge we've gained about plants to better understand the numerous woody giants that surround us.

When we observe a tree, we are taking notice of all its similarities and differences in comparison to other trees. That is, to better understand each tree, we must see what characteristics it shares with other trees, and what characteristics make it unique. We've already discussed many of the different categories we can use to distinguish trees. We can distinguish trees by their external structure, nature of leaves, type of flowers, type of fruit, etc.

When we begin the process of analyzing a tree, we can start by saying that all trees are, well, trees. By that we mean that trees are woody plants (not herbaceous) and have a primary stem (unlike shrubs). All trees share those characteristics. That being true, not all trees look exactly the same. One distinction we can make between trees is the shape of their crown.

The crown of a tree is made up of all the branches and leaves extending from the stem (essentially every part of the tree that is above ground—the tree's shoot system). Seven basic crown shapes can be observed. The first are columnar crowns, which have branches that grow vertically, close to the trunk, creating the appearance of a column. Oval crowns are similar to columnar but extend farther out to form more of an oval shape. Likewise, a rounded crown forms a structure closer to that of a circle. A crown with vertical branches that spread wide and create a structure similar to an upside-down triangle are said to be vase-shaped. Sort of in reverse, a tree's crown can have branches extending out wide at the base and growing narrower as you approach the pinnacle. These are said to be pyramidal (resembling the pyramids). Some trees have branches that extend out horizontally from the trunk. This would be an example of a spreading crown. Finally, there are also some trees whose branches look too heavy to hold up. These ground-sweeping branches almost make the tree appear dejected or sad. Hence, this structure is appropriately called a weeping crown.

The next thing that is easy to notice is the size of the tree. Is the tree really tall? Is it rather short? How thick is the trunk? Some trees that remain small are used as decoration for lawns and buildings. These are called ornamental trees. We can also observe whether the tree loses its leaves in the fall or maintains them, and is thus deciduous or evergreen. From this point we can study the size and shape of the leaves and categorize them based on the characteristics we learned earlier. We can repeat this same process with the tree's flowers, fruits, and bark.

These questions and observations make us familiar with the tree and help us identify it. Identifying trees is an entertaining and beneficial enterprise that makes us more aware of the world we encounter every day. We can identify a tree by observing all its unique features and comparing them to a tree guide. A tree guide is a booklet that lists all the different types of trees in a region or continent. It catalogs all the distinguishing attributes of various trees so that the observer can compare them to the specific trees he encounters. The guide can also supply

round   oval

pyramid   column   spreading

vase   weeping

Figure 44: Types of Crowns

61

information about the tree that you may not be able to discern just by observation. It can tell you the average height of that particular type of tree or where they are normally found. The location and climate in which a tree is commonly found is called its natural habitat. For

example, evergreens (specifically conifers) are often found in colder climates because they can endure the extreme temperatures and fewer hours of sunlight. Trees like the sycamore require a lot of water, and are thus often located near rivers and streams.

Once you have identified a tree, you are free to investigate all the interesting facts associated with that tree. Perhaps you now know the tree in your front yard is an ash. It may be interesting to know that the majority of baseball bats are manufactured from the wood that comes from ash trees. Or maybe you observe a sycamore and learn that the reason for its flaky bark is because the bark doesn't grow as the tree grows and new bark must be grown for the old, which peels and falls off. There are so many interesting things to learn about the trees that inhabit your own neighborhood. Beyond your neighborhood, there are amazing trees all around the world. In California there is a redwood tree called Hyperion which holds the world's height record at 379 feet!

Figure 45: Sequoia Trees

That's taller than the Statue of Liberty. There is also a tree near Oaxaca, Mexico, whose trunk is 37 feet in diameter. It would take more than 23 sixth graders just to reach around it! This Montezuma cypress has knots and gnarls that almost resemble animals caught in the tree. These figures have earned this tree the nickname "The Tree of Life."

Figure 46: "The Tree of Life"

From oxygen to food to treehouses, trees play a vital role in the life of humans and of all life on this planet. A healthy curiosity will not be disappointed when it is employed to gain familiarity with these amazing plants.

ADVANCED WORK

CHAPTER 8

Photosynthesis

We now know where the process of photosynthesis takes place, and we know the result of the process is food, but what exactly is photosynthesis? The Greek origin of this complex term may once again be an aid in understanding this process. Photosynthesis is a combination of two Greek words: φῶς (**phos**, or *photo*) and σύνθεσις (**synthesis**). *Photo* is a term that means "light." When you take a photograph, you are using light to make a "graph" or "writing" of the image you see (γραφή meaning "writing"). Your camera exposes the film to the light and captures the image. *Synthesis* is a term that means "to bring together." So, then, photosynthesis is a process of bringing things together by the means of light. The question is: Just what exactly is being brought together?

Everything around you (and in you) is made of tiny building blocks called **atoms**. You can think of an atom as being somewhat like a Lego block. Not every Lego, nor every atom, is the same. Legos come in a multitude of sizes, shapes, and colors. The different types of atoms are called **elements**. This is similar to taking all your Legos and separating them based on how many knobs they have and how those knobs are arranged on the block. So atoms are the building blocks, and an element is a particular kind of atom. For example, all hydrogen atoms are the same.

All the different elements have been organized by scientists into a chart called the **Periodic Table**. Some elements are normally found combined to each other.

Oxygen, for example, is usually found as a combination of two oxygen atoms [O_2, or dioxygen - Greek δίς (**dis, di**), meaning "twice" or "two"].

Just as with Legos, different combinations of elements can create a variety of things. For instance, there is an element called hydrogen that exists by itself as a gas. When two hydrogen atoms (H) are combined with an oxygen atom (O), even though they are both gases, they form a molecule of H_2O, or what is better known as water. A molecule is a combination of two or more atoms. A molecule can have any number of atoms (building blocks) or number of elements (types of building blocks). So if we look at oxygen again, it normally exists as the molecule O_2. It is a molecule because it has more than one atom connected to each other, but it only has one element present (two atoms of the oxygen type). A carbon dioxide (CO_2) molecule has three atoms present, two of which are the element oxygen and one of which is the element carbon.

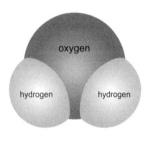

Figure 47: H₂O molecule

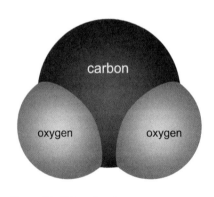

Figure 48: CO₂ molecule

Perhaps from the information we have just discussed, you have already figured out the answer to our previous question. Elements and molecules are the things that are being brought together in photosynthesis. Photosynthesis uses light to separate molecules into their elements and then brings the elements together in a distinct way to form different molecules. Going back to our Lego analogy, it would be like taking a Lego car apart and then reassembling

Periodic Table of the Elements

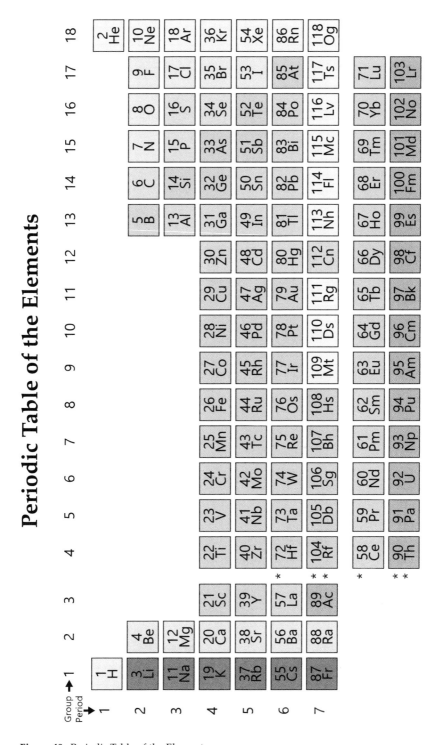

Figure 49: Periodic Table of the Elements

the blocks to form a tower instead. In photosynthesis, water molecules (H_2O) and carbon dioxide molecules (CO_2) are split apart into their elements and then recombined to form oxygen (O_2) and a substance called glucose ($C_6H_{12}O_6$).

To be more specific, water is brought to the cell from the xylem, and carbon dioxide is removed from the air circulating

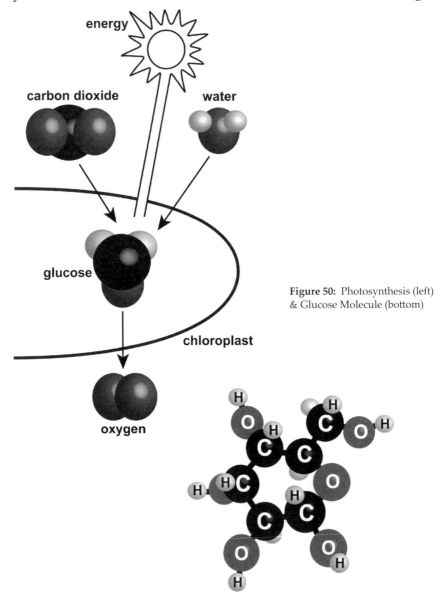

energy

carbon dioxide

water

glucose

chloroplast

oxygen

Figure 50: Photosynthesis (left) & Glucose Molecule (bottom)

around the mesophyll. The water and carbon dioxide are drawn into the chloroplast, where the chlorophyll uses the energy from the sunlight to split the water molecule into hydrogen and oxygen. Since the oxygen taken from the water molecule isn't needed, it is released back into the air circulating the mesophyll, and, subsequently, out of the leaf into the atmosphere. The hydrogen is then combined with the carbon dioxide to form glucose. When the hydrogen is added, some of the oxygen from the carbon dioxide is also released.

If we extend our analogy further, you could say that Lego boats (water) and Lego planes (carbon dioxide) are brought into a factory (chloroplast). Inside this factory is a special machine (chlorophyll) that can take the Legos apart and rearrange them into something different. Using a powerful energy source (sunlight), the machine breaks the Lego boat down into its individual blocks. It then takes some of those blocks, and after disassembling the plane, adds some of the boat blocks to the plane blocks. Once the machine is done, it now has a Lego that doesn't look like a boat or a plane. Instead the machine has made a Lego cheeseburger (glucose). However, there are still some blocks (oxygen) left over from the boat and plane. Because the machine has no use for the extra pieces, it tosses them out of the factory.

That story may still be a little confusing. We can take the same information about photosynthesis and simplify it into what is called a **chemical equation**. A chemical equation just takes the molecules the process starts out with (the **reactants**) and shows what molecules are left at the end of the process (the **products**). It puts this information in a simple formula that resembles a math equation. The chemical equation for photosynthesis looks like this:

You may notice that the H_2O and the CO_2 both have sixes in front of them. This is because it takes six water

$$\overbrace{6\ CO_2 + 6\ H_2O}^{\text{reactants}} \rightarrow \overbrace{C_6H_{12}O_6 + 6\ O_2}^{\text{products}}$$

molecules and 6 carbon dioxide molecules to form one glucose molecule. Those little subscript numbers next to the letters tell how many atoms of that element make up that molecule. A water molecule has two hydrogen atoms (H_2) and one oxygen atom (O). A carbon dioxide molecule has one carbon atom (C) and two oxygen atoms (O_2). A glucose molecule ($C_6H_{12}O_6$) is a large molecule with six carbon atoms (C_6), twelve hydrogen atoms (H_{12}), and six oxygen atoms (O_6). The trick to a chemical equation is that it has to have the same number of atoms on both sides. If you look at the reactants, there are six water molecules, meaning there are twelve hydrogens (H_2 = 2 hydrogens, 2 x 6 = 12) and six oxygen atoms (O = 1 oxygen, 1 x 6 = 6). There are also six carbon dioxide atoms, meaning there are six carbon atoms and twelve more oxygen. That means the total for the reactants is six carbon atoms, twelve hydrogen atoms, and eighteen oxygen atoms. On the product side, all the carbons and hydrogens are accounted for in the glucose ($C_6H_{12}O_6$), but only six out of the eighteen oxygens are accounted for. If you remember, oxygen atoms always like to be combined with another oxygen atom. That is why you don't see twelve oxygen atoms in the product but six O_2 (6 x 2 = 12). Since glucose is what is called a simple sugar, in remembering the chemical equation for photosynthesis, it may be helpful to think:

"six, six; sugar and six"

Glucose, as a simple sugar, is used by plants and animals as energy and for the production of important

reactants	products

$$6\ CO_2 + 6\ H_2O \rightarrow C_6H_{12}O_6 + 6\ O_2$$

6 Carbon	6 Carbon
18 Oxygen	18 Oxygen
12 Hydrogen	12 Hydrogen

materials. Plants use the glucose they make and the minerals attained from the soil to produce the proteins, fats, vitamins, cellulose, and other materials they need. Some of the glucose in plants is converted into a substance called **sucrose**, which is the technical name for table sugar. It is sucrose that the phloem distributes throughout the plant and which makes tree sap sweet to taste.

CHAPTER 9

Respiration

Have you ever been using a remote control that suddenly stopped working? Or perhaps you have gone a long time without eating and for some reason you just want to take a nap. In both the cases, the factor that is missing is energy. All creatures need energy in order to live and function. Every time you blink your eyes, move your hand, or even think with your mind, you are using energy. The greatest source of energy is the sun. However, humans and animals aren't solar-powered. That is, you can't just go stand in the sun and get energy. Most likely you'll find that by standing in the sunlight, you grow more and more fatigued instead. This is why the process of photosynthesis performed in plants is so important. That simple sugar, glucose, which is produced by the plants, is actually a harnessed form of the sun's energy. Every living creature, including plants themselves, uses the energy stored in glucose to perform the functions they need to survive.

When glucose is brought into the cell of a living creature, a process is performed that splits the glucose molecule and releases the stored energy. The energy it gains makes it possible for that cell to fulfill its role within the body of the organism. The process of releasing energy from glucose for use in the cell is called cellular **respiration**. Cellular respiration is essentially the process of photosynthesis in reverse. Photosynthesis uses the energy from the sun to bind carbon dioxide and water, forming glucose and oxygen. Whereas, in cellular respiration, glucose reacts with oxygen, releasing the stored energy and giving carbon dioxide and water as by-products. You can see this illustrated in the chemical equation below.

$$C_6H_{12}O_6 + 6\ O_2 \rightarrow 6\ CO_2 + 6\ H_2O + energy$$

Notice that the chemical equation for respiration has the same molecules as photosynthesis and in the same amounts, only the reactants and products have switched. The process demonstrated by this chemical equation is specifically referred to as **aerobic respiration**. It is called this because it uses oxygen to break up the glucose. The term *aerobic* means "requiring oxygen" (literally, "air for life") and again comes from the combination of two Greek words: ἀήρ, meaning "air," and βίος, which means "life."

A process very similar to this is demonstrated when baking bread. You may have noticed the phenomenon of bread rising once all the ingredients have been mixed together. This effect is the result of a type of cellular respiration called **fermentation**. Fermentation is a type of respiration because it also is a process that releases the energy contained in glucose. Unlike aerobic respiration, however, it does not use oxygen to break up the glucose molecule. If you have ever made bread, you know that an essential ingredient (particularly if you want fluffy bread) is something called **yeast**. Yeast is actually a single-celled organism that lives off of glucose molecules. In fermentation, yeast is used instead of oxygen to break up the glucose molecules. Just like aerobic respiration, one of the products of fermentation is carbon dioxide gas. It is this gas that causes the bread to rise.

Fermentation is not as effective as aerobic respiration in breaking up glucose for energy. As a result, instead of water, fermentation produces molecules that still contain some stored energy. This product is called alcohol (C_2H_5OH). This molecule still contains carbon, which means that fermentation also produces less carbon dioxide than aerobic respiration. When baking bread, the alcohol gets cooked out while the bread is in the oven. The baking off of the alcohol in the dough is part of what causes the wonderful smell that is customary in baking bread. The chemical equation for fermentation is very similar to aerobic respiration, except in the reactants you replace oxygen with yeast, and in the products you replace water with alcohol.

$$C_6H_{12}O_6 + yeast \rightarrow 2\ C_2H_5OH + 2\ CO_2 + energy$$

It is aerobic respiration that is performed in the cells of plants and animals in order to harness the energy in glucose. Plants must use the glucose they produce in the leaves to power the cellular processes in the rest of the plant. Plants and animals need a consistent supply of the energy stored in glucose for their cellular processes. The energy plants and animals get from respiration is called **food energy**. Food energy comes in three forms: **sugars**, **starches**, and **cellulose**. All three forms are referred to as **carbohydrates**. They received this name because they all come from glucose, which is essentially a combination of carbon (carbo) and water (hydrate). *Carbohydrate* literally means "watered carbon." That may be confusing since a glucose molecule seems more complicated. Yet, you may notice that glucose, $C_6H_{12}O_6$, has twice as many hydrogens (12) as carbons and oxygens (both 6). You can simplify the relationship of carbons and oxygens to hydrogens by writing it as CH_2O (or $C+H_2O$). Hence, molecules that possess this basic ratio of one carbon (C) for every hydrate (H_2O) are said to be carbohydrates.

Sugars are the simplest forms of carbohydrates and are used to directly supply energy to the plant or animal. **Glucose** is the most common type of simple sugar. Glucose is called a simple sugar because it exists as a single molecule. A simple sugar is any molecule that has the formula

$C_6H_{12}O_6$. Simple sugars are ready energy, meaning that a plant or animal does not have to change the composition of the molecule in order for the cell to use it in respiration. You may wonder why it would be necessary to say that every simple sugar has the formula $C_6H_{12}O_6$. Every simple sugar is just glucose, right? Actually, glucose is not the only simple sugar. The simple sugar found in fruit is called **fructose**. Simple sugars, like fructose, have the same chemical formula as glucose ($C_6H_{12}O_6$), but the atoms are arranged in different ways. The atoms of glucose are connected to each other in a particular way. This structure can be rearranged when glucose is put to a particular use. **Galactose** is another example of a simple sugar (found in milk).

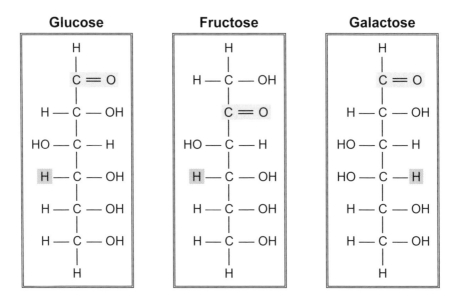

Figure 51: Simple Sugars

Simple sugars are also referred to as **monosaccharides**. This large term simply means "single sugar," from the Greek μονος (**monos**), meaning "single," and σάκχαρ (**saccher**), meaning "sugar." This is because, as mentioned above, monosaccharides exist as individual molecules of sugar, ready to be burned for energy. You may hear the term *sugar* and think of the crystals that transform boring breakfast cereal into a sweet treat, or the substance that makes cookies so tasty. That crystal form only occurs when two simple sugars are combined. Table sugar (called **sucrose**) is actually a combination of the two monosaccharides glucose and fructose. You may remember that tree sap is made of sucrose. Because sucrose is a combination of two monosaccharides, it is called a **disaccharide**. You may have already guessed that this term just substitutes the prefix **mono** (meaning "one") for the prefix **di** (meaning "two"). You can easily recognize the disaccharide sucrose, but other common disaccharides are **lactose** (milk sugar) and **maltose** (malt sugar). Disaccharides, like monosaccharides, are also a quick form of energy for plants and animals. The only difference is that disaccharides must be broken apart into their simple sugars before they can be used by the cell.

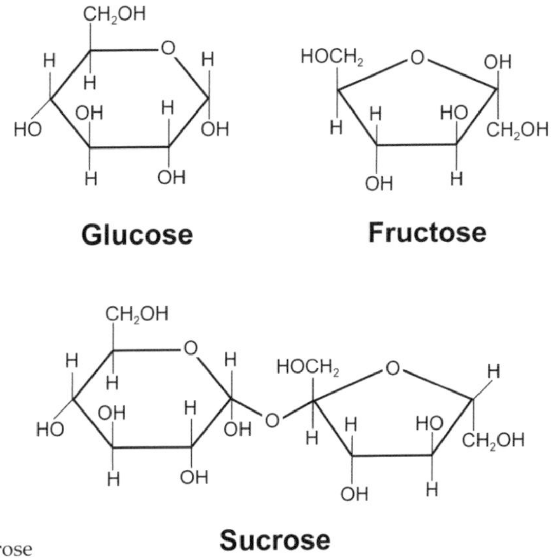

Glucose   Fructose

Figure 52: Sucrose   **Sucrose**

You may have wondered during our discussion on fermentation just where the glucose comes from when baking bread. The glucose that the yeast breaks up comes from two disaccharides: sucrose and maltose. We just discovered that sucrose is a combination of the simple sugars glucose and fructose. Maltose, which comes from the flour, is actually a combination of two glucose molecules. The water in the bread recipe actually dissolves (splits up) the sucrose and some of the maltose molecules so that the yeast can get to the individual glucose molecules.

Plants survive by constantly burning the simple sugars provided by the leaves. You may wonder what happens at night when plants no longer have the sun to use for photosynthesis. Fortunately, according to their brilliant design, plants produce more glucose than they immediately need and store the rest for later use. Plants do this by linking a bunch of glucose units together to form large energy storage molecules called starches. **Starches** are carbohydrates that are made of a combination of many simple sugars. Because they include many sugars, they are called **polysaccharides** ("poly" comes from the Greek πολύς, meaning "many"). In fact, whereas a disaccharide consists of two simple sugars linked together, a starch will consist of 300-1000 glucose units joined together. The complex arrangement of a starch requires a longer process for separating it into its smaller units of sugar. This makes starches a long-term source of energy, whereas sugars provide a quick source of energy.

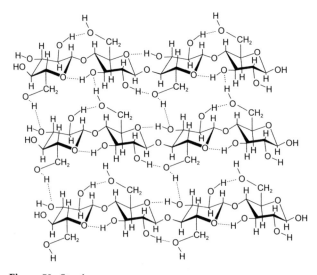

Figure 53: Starch

This is why when you eat food with a lot of sugars (or simple carbohydrates), such as a cookie, your digestive system quickly breaks them up and sends glucose through your blood to the rest of your body. As a result, you usually feel a rush of energy that quickly dissipates. However, if you have food that has starches (**complex carbohydrates**), such as potatoes, rice, or wheat, your digestive system will spend more time breaking down the complex storage molecules, and you will feel a steady flow of energy that will last much longer. The special molecules that break starches apart are called **enzymes**.

Enzymes break complex carbohydrates down into their simple sugars. Different enzymes exist in different organisms. Trees have enzymes that break up the sucrose flowing through the phloem, so that the cells can use the glucose for energy. Humans and animals have digestive systems that possess different enzymes for breaking down food. The saliva in your mouth has enzymes that start breaking down complex carbohydrates while you are chewing. That is why when you chew a piece of bread (starch), you will start to taste the sweetness of the maltose. The enzymes have split the polysaccharides into the individual sugars, which are characteristically sweet.

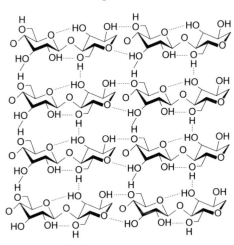

Figure 54: Cellulose

The third type of carbohydrate (or food energy) is called **cellulose**. You may remember that cellulose is what constitutes the walls of plant cells. Cellulose is a polysaccharide that is composed of a chain of glucose rings even larger and more complex than starch molecules. A cellulose molecule can consist of 1,500 linked glucose molecules. This massive cluster of glucose is a part of every cell in a plant and provides a major source of stored energy.

This fact may make your mind start turning. If plants are basically made out of cellulose, and cellulose is made out of glucose (simple sugar), are plants and vegetables essentially sugar? Yes! So the next time you have a hankering for something sweet, eat some celery! Okay, that's not quite true. Plants are essentially made of sugar, but you may notice that some don't seem very sweet when you eat them. This is because humans actually lack the enzyme that can break cellulose down into its simple sugars. On the contrary, many animals *do* have the enzyme that can break down cellulose. This is why many animals get most of their food energy from eating plants. For humans to receive the energy stored in cellulose, they must have broken down some of the cellulose by cooking the plant, or consume animals that have already broken it down into useful glucose. The heat applied to the plant breaks down some of the cellulose, which is why cooked vegetables are sweeter (or at least less bitter) than uncooked vegetables. The cellulose that humans cannot break down does provide fiber, which is a necessary part of our diet. Vegetables also have essential vitamins and minerals that humans can digest, which is why they are such an important part of a healthy diet. That is also why, even though both are made of glucose, cookies are not a sufficient substitute for vegetables.

Photo Credits

The following photos have been used under Creative Commons from the photographers listed.

- Figure 11, Running Vine by Flickr.com user *woodleywonderworks*
- Figure 14, Flaky Bark – Sycamore by Flickr.com user *bobistraveling*
- Figure 14, Scaly Bark – Silver Maple by Flickr.com user *romana klee*
- Figure 14, Warty Bark – Hackberry by Flickr.com user *Dendroica cerulea*
- Figure 17, Broadleaf by Flickr.com user *Marcy Reiford*
- Figure 18, Needle-leaf by Flickr.com user *Horia Varlan*
- Figure 24, Maple Leaf by Flickr.com user *jfh686*
- Figure 24, Double-toothed Leaf by Flickr.com user *Dendroica cerulea*
- Figure 28, Leaves that Have Changed Color by Flickr.com user *OregonDOT*
- Figure 39, Female and Male Pinecones by Flickr.com user *JohnGiez-*
- Figure 40, Bee Covered in Pollen *by* Flickr.com user *ForestWander*
- Figure 44, Apple Center by Flickr.com user *Artotem*
- Figure 47, Acorn by Flickr.com user *PhylB*
- Figure 49, Wheat by Flickr.com user *Dag Terje Filip Endresen*
- Figure 52, Round Tree by Flickr.com user *MGSpiller*
- Figure 52, Oval Tree by Flickr.com user *Bruce Martin*
- Figure 52, Column Tree by Flickr.com user *di bo di*
- Figure 52, Vase Tree by Flickr.com user *wlcutler*
- Figure 52, Spreading Tree by Flickr.com user *Aah-Yeah*
- Figure 52, Weeping Willow Tree by Flickr.com user *Wolfgang Lonien*
- Figure 53, Sequoia Trees by Flickr.com user *Tobias*
- Figure 54, The Tree of Life by Flickr.com user *fer tapia*